The Standard Publishing Company, Cincinnati, Ohio
A division of Standex International Corporation
Printed in the United States of America
00 99 98 97 96 95 94 93   5 4 3 2 1

ISBN 0-7847-0064-8
Cataloging-in-Publication data available
Designed by Coleen Davis

Standard Publishing
Cincinnati, Ohio

- A -
1 • 2 • 3
CHRISTMAS

written by
Diane Stortz

illustrated by
Nancy Munger

What child is this, who, laid to rest,
On Mary's lap is sleeping?
Whom angels greet with anthems sweet,
While shepherds watch are keeping?

This, this is Christ the king,
Whom shepherds guard and angels sing.
Haste, haste to bring him laud,
The babe, the Son of Mary.

—William C. Dix

1 one holy child

2 two happy people

See within a manger laid
Jesus, Lord of heaven and earth.
Mary, Joseph, lend your aid,
With us sing our Savior's birth.
—Traditional

So bring him incense, gold and myrrh,
Come rich and poor, to own him.
The King of kings, salvation brings,
Let loving hearts enthrone him.
—William C. Dix

3 three gifts for a king

4 four friendly beasts

Jesus our brother, strong and good,
Was humbly born in a stable rude,
And the friendly beasts around him stood,
Jesus our brother, strong and good.

—English carol, 12th century

It came upon the midnight clear,
    That glorious song of old,
From angels bending near the earth
    To touch their harps of gold.
—Edmund H. Sears

5 five harps of gold

6 six sleepy sheep

Sheep on the hillside lay
Whiter than snow,
Shepherds were watching them,
    Long, long ago.

—*Traditional*

seven surprised
shepherds

While shepherds watched
their flocks by night,
All seated on the ground,
The angel of the Lord
came down,
and glory shone around.
—*Nahum Tate*

O come, little children,
O come, one and all!
O come to the cradle
in Bethlehem's stall!
—*Christoph von Schmid*

8 eight eager children

9 nine gifts of love

Beside thy manger here I stand,
Dear Jesus, Lord, and Savior,
A gift of love within my hand
To thank thee for thy favor.

—Martin Luther

10 ten Christmas candles

Then be ye glad, good people,
This night of all the year,
And light ye up your candles:
His star is shining near.

—*Traditional*

11 eleven echoing bells

Oh, he did whistle and she did sing,
And all the bells on earth did ring,
For joy that our Savior he was born
On Christmas Day in the morning.

—old English carol

12 twelve
twinkling stars

For Christ is born of Mary;
And gathered all above,
While mortals sleep, the angels keep
Their watch of wond'ring love.
O morning stars, together
Proclaim the holy birth,
And praises sing to God the king,
And peace to men on earth.

—*Phillips Brooks*